The Guide to Owning

Millipedes and Centipedes

Jerry G. Walls

CONTENTS

Introducing Millipedes 3
Millipede Sex and Growth 13
General Care of Millipedes 25
Some Little Guys 34
Big Round Ones 44
Introducing Centipedes 56
Index 64

Title Page: Colorful Madagascan giant millipedes, perhaps *Aphistogoniulus*. Photo: R.D. Bartlett

My thanks to Dr. Richard L. Hoffman, Virginia Mus. Nat. Hist., for his comments over the years, and to Dr. Rowland M. Shelley, North Carolina State Mus., and Dr. Clifford S. Crawford for some important papers. Thanks also to Mark Smith, Robert Szymanski, and Gerard Dupre for specimens and comments. As usual, my special thanks go to Maleta, my wife, for her patience during photography and for constantly bugging me to take care of my animals.

RE 170

Distributed in the UNITED STATES to the Pet Trade by T.F.H. Publications, Inc., 1 TFH Plaza, Neptune City, NJ 07753; on the Internet at www.tfh.com; in CANADA by Rolf C. Hagen Inc., 3225 Sartelon St., Montreal, Quebec H4R 1E8; Pet Trade by H & L Pet Supplies Inc., 27 Kingston Crescent, Kitchener, Ontario N2B 2T6; in ENGLAND by T.F.H. Publications, PO Box 74, Havant PO9 5TT; in AUSTRALIA AND THE SOUTH PACIFIC by T.F.H. (Australia), Pty. Ltd., Box 149, Brookvale 2100 N.S.W., Australia; in NEW ZEALAND by Brooklands Aquarium Ltd., 5 McGiven Drive, New Plymouth, RD1 New Zealand; in SOUTH AFRICA by Rolf C. Hagen S.A. (PTY.) LTD., P.O. Box 201199, Durban North 4016, South Africa; in JAPAN by T.F.H. Publications, Japan—Jiro Tsuda, 10-12-3 Ohjidai, Sakura, Chiba 285, Japan. Published by T.F.H. Publications, Inc.
MANUFACTURED IN THE
UNITED STATES OF AMERICA
BY T.F.H. PUBLICATIONS, INC.

INTRODUCING MILLIPEDES

Why a book on such obscure groups as the millipedes and centipedes? I can come up with three very good reasons: one, they are sold in pet shops and have at least a few fanciers; two, there is no other work in book form that even attempts to cover the groups as pets to be kept by hobbyists; and three, I happen to like millipedes and have followed their taxonomy in a casual way for many years. If you also are interested in millipedes (and centipedes, though there is less emphasis on them in this book), then I hope that you will find some answers to your questions here. However, do not expect answers to everything—even the academic experts on the group seem to know very little about the natural history of the larger millipedes and how to keep them in captivity. I was not even able to obtain good answers on how long some of the most common American millipedes live as adults, and few experts even want to guess.

What follows can be considered a first attempt to familiarize hobbyists with the potential of millipedes as pets. I've kept about a dozen species for various lengths of time, some large and

Identification of most millipedes is complicated and uncertain. This large, striking Peruvian "cogwheel millipede" may belong in the family Platyrhacidae.

commercially available, others small and of limited interest to the average hobbyist. Overall, I've had limited success, though a few have reproduced in my terraria (though with little help on my part) and some seem to have lived decent lifetimes (I think). I admit to being confounded by some millipedes I've tried to keep and that I've been able to identify few with any great success because of lack of males or the appropriate literature. In the future some of these problems may be resolved, and I appreciate any help and additional information you can supply.

In the matter of identification, I will be glad to take a look at preserved specimens (males,

The two pairs of legs on every body segment show clearly in this giant African black millipede, *Archispirostreptus*.

Photo: M. Walls

preferably) from either the commercial trade or locally collected, but there are no promises. It was estimated over a decade ago that the about 6,000 species of millipedes so far described represent only a sixth (and probably even less than that) of the species that actually exist. Since then most of the taxonomic workers have retired or moved on to other fields, and only six or seven workers around the world are today trying to identify and describe millipedes. Even in the United States new species are described on a regular basis, as are new genera, and even the families are poorly understood. In the tropics almost anything could be new, and if a millipede is large and colorful, it will be shipped by commercial dealers whether described or not.

WHAT ARE MILLIPEDES?

Millipedes are elongated, multisegmented land-living arthropods that typically have two pairs of legs per external body segment. Many species are about 1 to 3 inches (25 to 75 mm) long, but there also are many tiny species under 0.2 inch (5 mm) in length that look like white threads and a few that are 6 to 10 inches (150 to 250 mm) long. The record length seems to be about 300 mm, held by several different spirostreptids (we'll talk about these later) from Africa and Asia. They are closely related to insects, and there are connecting links of a sort between the millipedes and the most primitive insects. They have a single pair of antennae, distinct jaws (two sets) that move from side to side (with some exceptions), and often (but not always) compound eyes formed by groups of simple ocelli above the bases of the antennae. Most millipedes have from 19 to over 100 pairs of legs, with the record apparently being about 375 pairs. No species has anything approaching the thousand legs implied by the term "millipede" (literally "thousand legs"). The legs have seven segments in most millipedes (but only six may be easily visible), though there may be reduced legs immediately behind the head, at the end of the body before the terminal (anal) segment, and on the seventh and eighth segments of males of most species.

Millipedes can be confused with some land crustaceans, the pillbugs or sowbugs, but these have only one pair of legs per segment, flattened gill plates at the bases of the legs that let the little animals breathe, and usually a pair of elongated, segmented uropods that extend back from the last segment. Insect larvae of various types all have at most three pairs of legs, though there may be false legs of various types on some of the segments, but never two pairs per segment. Centipedes have long projections from the last body segment, fang-like "jaws" with poison glands at their bases, and of course only one pair of legs per segment.

The millipedes have a long but spotty fossil record, with probable millipedes recorded from the Upper Silurian, some 400 million years ago. The largest land arthropod known was a millipede, *Arthropleura*, from the Carboniferous period, over 300 million years ago. These animals left tracks and fragmentary remains that indicate some may have reached lengths of almost 6 feet (1.8 meters) and widths of 1.5 feet (0.45 meter). They were replaced in later periods by giant pillbug-like millipedes with long spines. There actually are very few fossil records of modern millipedes, however, except for scraps found in fossil rodent nests, amber, and similar deposits.

STRUCTURE

Hobbyists aren't too interested in animal structure, as a rule, but in the case of the millipedes you have to know some basics to be able to identify your pets to at least major group. Millipedes have a distinct head, a trunk comprised of many body segments or *rings*, and a terminal or *anal segment* that lacks legs and is comprised to two movable plates, the *anal valves*. The head is polished, has a single pair of long and usually slender antennae that may be covered with fine hairs, and often has compound eyes located near the bases of the antennae. Eyes are absent in some groups and represented only by one or a few simple eyes (*ocelli*) in others. Many millipedes add eyes to the eye patch with each molt, and specialists can tell the approximate age of a juvenile millipede in some cases by counting eyes and noting their

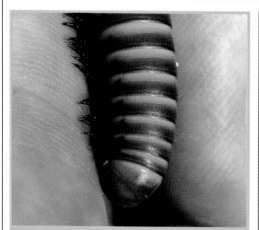

The tail-end of a western desert millipede, *Orthoporus ornatus*. The rounded anal valves are preceded by a ring called the telson.

Photo: M. Walls

arrangement. The eyes probably only detect movement, not actual images.

The actual jaws of a millipede are hidden by a large plate that is easily seen if you look under the head of a large millipede. This plate usually is called the *gnathochilarium* but really is an assembly of several different mouthparts that vary considerably with the major groups of millipedes. Generally there is a pair of strap-like *stipes* on each side of a single basal plate, the *mentum*, that often is triangular. Between the tips of the stipes are a pair of small *lingual plates*. The relative sizes and positions of these plates are taxonomically very important but difficult to see in a living specimen.

The first body segment behind the head is enlarged at least a bit to cover the back of the head and often is very large and somewhat inflated. This is the *collum*, and it is numbered as segment one. The collum does not bear legs. The first "real" segment is segment or ring two, which may or may not bear a single pair of legs. Segment two marks the location of the external sex organs, small slender or conical *penes* in males and usually flattened *sperm receptacles* through which the oviducts open in females. These sperm receptacles often can be used to identify female millipedes to species and are known in the technical literature as *cyphopods*, while the actual external openings of the oviducts are the vulvae. Both the penes and the cyphopods are small and located behind the bases of the legs.

The legs have seven segments, named from the base out as the: *coxa, trochanter* (often small and obscure), *prefemur, femur, postfemur, tibia,* and *tarsus*; there typically is a small claw at the end of each leg. There are two pairs of legs on most segments because each external ring of a millipede represents two true or internal segments that have become fused during the development of the

In flattened polydesmids, here the xystodesmid *Pachydesmus crassicutis* from Tennessee, the anal valves are under the body rather than at the tip.

Photo: M. Walls

Polydesmid millipedes typically lack eyes. In this view of *Pachydesmus crassicutis* you can see the wide collum behind the head and its tapered lower margin.

Photo: M. Walls

embryo. If you were to dissect a millipede you would find that each ring has two sets of muscles and nerve enlargements. If you look closely you can see that each solid-appearing ring actually is made of several smaller pieces with faint lines marking where they have fused. There typically are two pairs of legs from the fourth ring back to one to three segments before the anal valves. The ring before the anal segment is called the *telson* and often has a spine or other projection at the center back of the ring that may project well beyond the anal valves.

In males of almost all millipedes (except for two primitive groups we'll mention later), at least one pair of legs on the seventh ring is modified into gonopods, often very strange spiny prongs that are used to transfer sperm to the cyphopods of the female during mating. In many species other legs also may be modified into

gonopods, ranging from the posterior legs of segment six through to the legs of the eighth segment. The identification of millipedes is a study of their gonopods. In some types the details can be seen well enough with a handlens and low magnification (10X or so) to allow identification, but more often the gonopods have to be dissected out and mounted on slides to study under much higher magnification. A perusal of the technical literature will reveal a bewildering variety of gonopod modifications, from simple segmented spines to structures with half a dozen prongs and long segments coiled like watchsprings. Without males, identification of females is almost impossible. We'll discuss mating and growth in the next chapter.

The rings themselves typically fall into one of three shape categories. They may be circular or nearly so and virtually smooth except for fine ridges and pinpoint indentations (punctae); circular with raised ridges and knobs in regular rows, the details varying greatly with different groups; or nearly flat with projecting edges (the *paranota*) that may be spiny (serrated).

CLASSIFICATION

The millipedes form a class, Diplopoda, of the phylum Arthropoda, the invertebrates with jointed legs. Their internal classification still varies considerably from worker to worker, but we'll stick to a simple system here and recognize three subclasses for two very odd and atypical groups plus the typical millipedes.

The members of the subclass **Penicillata** or Pselaphognatha are tiny (2 to 4 mm long), soft-bodied millipedes that look a lot like insect larvae. They have only 11 or rarely 12 segments and 17 or fewer pairs of legs. Most have large tufts of long bristles in pairs on the body plus shorter bristles across the back of each segment. The penicillate order Polyxenida is represented through the drier tropical regions of the world, with some species extending north quite a bit. A few species occur in the United States and Europe, where they may be found under the loose bark of trees in small colonies easily recognized by the presence of many shed skins among the living animals. Unlike

An enrolled South African giant pill millipede, *Sphaerotherium* sp. These agile, tough millipedes may be common in gardens and are far larger than the few pill millipedes that occur in the U.S.

Photo: M. Walls

all other millipedes, penicillates lack gonopods. The male spins a web onto which he deposits a clump of sperm, the spermatophore. He then induces a female to pass over the spermatophore and pull it into her oviducts. Some species and populations of penicillates are parthenogenetic, males being absent or very rare and females laying unfertilized eggs that develop into female young. There are about 100 species in three families. The few United States species belong to the genus *Polyxenus* (except possibly one species in the Florida Keys).

The strange pill millipedes form subclass **Pentazonia**, tiny to very large millipedes with oval bodies usually capable of rolling into balls. The small species may look a great deal like true crustacean pillbugs, but of course they have two pairs of legs per segment. The species are mostly tropical (three genera with a few poorly known species are known from the southern United States). Surprisingly, some of the gigantic pills from South Africa and Madagascar occasionally are imported for the hobby. These may reach 4 inches (100 mm) in length, with a width almost half the length. The legs appear weak, but the last two pairs of the male are heavier and end in obvious pincers. Males lack typical gonopods, instead backing up to a female, rolling her over and then "squeaking" at her by rubbing ridged plates together. The female recognizes the squeaks and unrolls, at which point the male

Madagascan giant pill millipedes, *Globotherium*, may be over 2 inches wide. Most are greenish, but some have attractive red accents. Because these animals feed on algae and fungi growing on trees as well as rotting wood, they may be difficult to maintain.

turns her over and the animals position themselves so their second segments are almost adjacent. He then uses his pincer-like legs to pull apart the edges of her cyphopods so sperm packets can flow from his penes into the female's vulvae.

South African giant pill millipedes belong to the genus *Sphaerotherium*, while those from Madagascar probably are genus *Globotherium*. Other giant pills occur in Australia. The African and Madagascan pills often are greenish. At night (and sometimes during the day) they may climb small shrubs and be found several feet above the ground. They seem to feed on algae and fungi growing on branches as well as on rotting wood and other plant parts. The jaws are very strong and the gut is long, obvious adaptations to eating rough food. They may live several years and generally are considered hard to care for. Their odd appearance and great bulk for a millipede make them desirable though usually expensive imports. The Pentazonia plus the Helminthomorpha often are treated as a single subclass, the **Chilognatha**, contrasted to the Penicillata or Pselaphognatha.

The remaining millipedes all belong to the subclass **Helminthomorpha**, the typical millipedes, in which one or more pairs of legs on and near the seventh segment are modified as gonopods in the males. Most are at least somewhat elongated, though some are broad and even

Few millipedes of the subclass Helminthomorpha are available, and most are too small for pets. The highly sculptured, flattened species of *Brachycybe*, however, fare moderately well in captivity.

capable of rolling into a ball. Many have spines and other processes on the rings. There is a great deal of variation in the mouthparts and head structures, and about 11 orders with some 100 families and over 5,000 species currently are recognized, many known from only one collection. Ten major orders contain the majority of species and all the species in the United States, but few are of even potential interest to hobbyists because of their small size and often very cryptic (hidden or secretive) habits.

Order Polyzoniida contains small species less than an inch (25 mm) long with very simple gonopods that are barely distinguishable from normal legs. Some have a distinctive camphor-like smell when disturbed. Order Julida contains the wireworm millipedes, typically small (1 to 2 inches, 25 to 50 mm), very narrow, cylindrical millipedes that may be abundant in the soil. Many species are "tramps," having been introduced around the world with plants, but others have very small ranges. Order Siphonophorida contains tropical species with the mouthparts modified into a sucking beak. Order Platydesmida contains a variety of small, sometimes brightly colored species with odd body shapes, including the bright pink species of *Brachycybe* that we'll mention later. Order Callipodida contains the crested millipedes, often of rather large size; we'll mention the genus *Abacion* in a later chapter. Order Chordeumatidae contains other crested or at least ridged millipedes of often tiny size and with three spinnerets at the end of the body to spin silk. They may be exceedingly abundant in the soil and also are a prominent portion of the cave-dwelling millipedes.

The larger millipedes belong mostly to three orders. The **Spirobolida** includes several families that reach a large enough size to attract attention. It includes the families Spirobolidae, Floridobolidae, and Atopetholidae, among others, all at least potentially of interest to hobbyists. The ventral part of the third segment is closed and there is only one pair of legs on segment five. The eyes usually are well-developed and in the form of a large circular patch above the antennal base. Additionally, the mentum of the gnathochilarium is large and triangular, and the lingual lamina are small, completely separated, and often hard to see. These all are

A gorgeously colored xystodesmid, order Polydesmida, from Tennessee. The southern Appalachians are home to many genera and species of these flattened millipedes, but they often are confusingly alike in coloration. This may be an *Apheloria* species.

Photo: M. Smith

cylindrical millipedes with many segments (about 35 to 60). Both sets of legs on the male seventh segment are modified as gonopods and often hidden inside the body when not active. Many large and colorful forms could theoretically be imported for the hobby, but they are very difficult to identify. *Narceus, Chicobolus,* and *Tylobolus* are familiar genera from the United States.

The order **Spirostreptida** is a gigantic tropical group with many large species. They are cylindrical species much like spirobolids at first glance, but the third segment is open ventrally, there are two pairs of legs on the fifth segment, and the mentum of the gnathochilarium is smaller and more rectangular, the lingual lamina larger and often in contact, not separated by the mentum. Additionally, the eyes often consist of just a few ocelli that are arranged in a curve around the base of the antenna. There may be up to 90 segments in these sometimes very large millipedes. Though few are colorful, their large size makes them popular in the terrarium hobby, and we will discuss several types in a later chapter.

The last major order of interest to hobbyists is the flattened **Polydesmida**, some of which reach 2 inches (50 mm) or more. They make up for their rather small size by the depressed shape with wide extensions to the side, the paranota, and often bright colors. With few exceptions, the body is comprised of only 20 (rarely 19 or 21) rings in adults, the telson often produced into a point. Eyes are absent in these litter inhabitants, but the antennae are long and quite flexible, with special sense organs. The males have the anterior set of legs on the seventh segment modified into gonopods that often take the form of curled blades. Like the spirobolids and spirostreptids, we'll discuss the polydesmids in a bit more detail later. Few species exceed 5 inches (125 mm) in length, and all are short-lived as adults, usually dying after mating and laying eggs.

For a good if somewhat technical overview of the millipede families, try to obtain a copy of Prof. Richard L. Hoffman's contribution in volume 2 of *Synopsis and Classification of Living Organisms*, McGraw Hill, New York, 1982 (S. Parker, editor). For a general guide to the biology of millipedes you might try *The Biology of Millipedes*, Oxford Science Publ., New York, 1992 (S. P. Hopkin and H. J. Read), though this book is more interested in microscopic structure and physiology than natural history and diversity and will be a tough read for most hobbyists. English hobbyists might try to find a copy of *Millipedes*, Synopses of the British Fauna, No. 35, 1985 (J. G. Blower), an excellently illustrated guide to all the British species (many also introduced into the United States).

So much for the generalities of millipedes. Let's move on to some more practical stuff, mating and growth, which in millipedes can be very complicated and deserve their own chapter.

MILLIPEDE SEX AND GROWTH

Unlike most vertebrate animals where classifications are based on details of size, color, and lengths or numbers of structures, much of the taxonomy of the arthropods (insects, spiders, millipedes, and the multitudes of other animals with jointed legs) is based on the structure of their sexual organs. Millipedes follow this trend and, if anything, enlarge upon it. You cannot accurately identify a typical millipede without having a male with fully developed gonopods. Like many other arthropods, millipedes spend most of their life as larvae, becoming sexually mature adults for only a (sometimes small) portion of the total lifetime of the individual. Adults are made for sex, while the more important larvae are made for feeding and thus for helping recycle the dead wood, leaves, and other plants that cover much of the earth. Millipedes are creatures of the leaf litter and pass their entire lives there, with very few exceptions.

FIRST, SOME SEX

Before you can have young, you have to have sex. Like almost all higher invertebrates, millipedes

Ventral view of a Madagascan giant pill millipede. These animals lack legs modified for sperm transfer in the male (gonopods), though males have pincer-like ends on some legs to help turn the female over for mating.

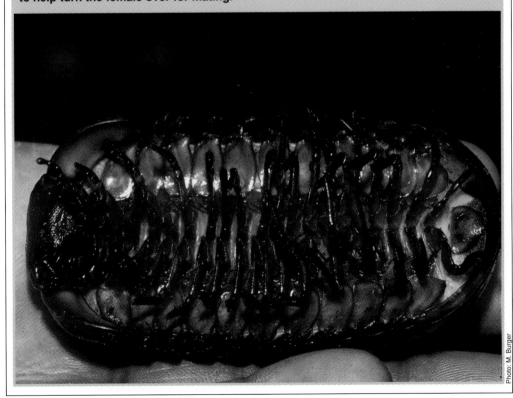

Photo: M. Burger

The **cyphopods of this female xystodesmid, _Pachydesmus crassicutis_, are barely visible under the serrated flanges to either side of the bases of the first large pair of legs, on segment two.**

Photo: M. Walls

(we'll deal only with the advanced millipedes, the Helminthomorpha, here; the other two groups are discussed in the introductory chapter) have two separate sexes, with a few exceptions, male and female. The primary sex organs are the ovaries and testes. The female ovaries are paired and internal, as you might expect. The male testes also are paired, but they tend to be elongated tubes that may run almost the entire length of the body. In both sexes the secondary sex organs, the penes and the openings for the oviducts, the vulvae, are on the lower surface of the body in the second segment. The penes are paired tubercles that generally are simple cones, rather fleshy and often off-white in color. They are inconspicuous at best in most millipedes. The vulvae are more obvious because each is within a distinct chamber, the cyphopod, which often is ornamented with spines and flanges and may be milky white and quite

conspicuous in breeding females. Usually the cyphopods also serve as sperm receptacles, and they may even have small lids or flaps (the opercula) serving to close them before and after mating.

Male millipedes produce their sperm in small gelatinous packets called spermatophores. These are excreted from the penes and molded into shape by the anterior legs, which also carry them back to the bases of the legs of the seventh segment, the gonopods, that are modified to transmit the spermatophores to the female's vulvae. Though the seventh legs are the actual intromittent organs (the equivalent of the mammalian penis or the reptilian hemipenes), they are only accessory sex organs because no sex products originate within or on them. Remember, sperm comes from the second segment and has to be manually transferred to the seventh segment.

GONOPODS

I don't want to make this a course in millipede identification, so I can't afford here to go into details about gonopods. Suffice it to say that a primitive or little-specialized gonopod, like those in many of the polydesmids or flat millipedes, still looks a lot like a regular leg, though with the proportions of all the segments changed a bit. The basal coxae usually are greatly enlarged, and the femurs often are elongated and have developed secondary branches and spines as well as other ornaments such as pads of hairs. A sperm duct, an open

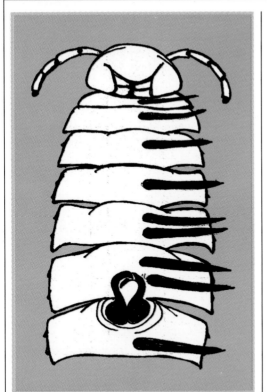

Diagram of the lower (ventral) side of a male polydesmid millipede showing a single pair of simple gonopods on the seventh segment.

adult gonopods, which has happened occasionally.

In many millipedes, including most of the large round ones, the true gonopods (the modified legs with sperm ducts) may be assisted by one or even two pairs of secondary gonopods, accessory accessory sex organs, if you will. These secondary gonopods may be as complicated as regular gonopods and even larger, with hoods to help hide the gonopods and extensions to strengthen them. Often the bases of the legs in front of and behind the gonopods also are enlarged and otherwise modified to help the

Diagram of the side (lateral view) of a male round millipede (Spirobolida or Spirostreptida) with both pairs of legs on segment seven modified as gonopods. Also, a leg pair from segment six is reduced or missing.

groove, runs from the base of the coxa to the tip of what usually is the longest part of the femur. It is into this sperm duct that the male manipulates spermatophores, and they travel up the duct to the female openings. Gonopods develop early in the life of a male millipede as small bumps in the positions of the regular legs. They are not fully developed until the millipede has molted through the last larval stage, though in some millipedes there may be poorly developed gonopods one molt before the terminal molt. Such poorly developed gonopods have led to lots of trouble in taxonomy when they have been misinterpreted as male hold the female in position to transfer sperm. Additionally, in many millipedes the anterior legs may be developed as pincers to hold the female, and the jaws may be enlarged and heavier than those of the female because they help hold the head of the female during mating for better control. Males of some millipedes are excessively modified for sex.

A few puzzling cases are known of male millipedes that lack gonopods entirely yet are perfectly normal for the species. The best examples of these are some Chinese and Central American species that also are covered with heavy spines on the rings of the body but lack all traces of gonopods. I'm not sure if anyone has yet determined how they mate. Additionally, since gonopods are just modified legs, occasional freak individuals of almost any species fail to develop full gonopods. Such oddballs may have a gonopod on one side of the body and a regular or nearly regular leg on the other side of the pair. Other oddballs have been recorded with extra gonopods, where more anterior or posterior legs have become gonopods rather than normal legs. Apparently any such oddball may have a normal sexlife.

TELLING MALE FROM FEMALE

First, kill the specimen, preserve it in alcohol, and using forceps (tweezers), separate the seventh segment of the body from the neighboring segments. Remove one of the gonopods, noting its orientation, and put it in a depression slide with a drop of alcohol. After examining it, drawing or photographing it from various angles (all carefully stated in comparison to the plane of the body axis), return it to a tiny vial with alcohol or mount it in euparol or a similar medium on a permanent slide.

OK, so that won't work for a hobbyist. First, you don't have the equipment to do it, and second, you obviously don't want to kill the specimen. (Of course, all specimens that die should be preserved immediately, preferably before they fall apart into separate segments; regular 70% rubbing alcohol works well, but you will have to change it at least twice during the first week or so as it becomes discolored.) So how do you tell a living male millipede from a living female?

It's sometimes easy. Turn the

Two male *Tylobolus* with the gonopods pulled into the body but displaying the modifications of the seventh ring and absence of true legs in their sex.

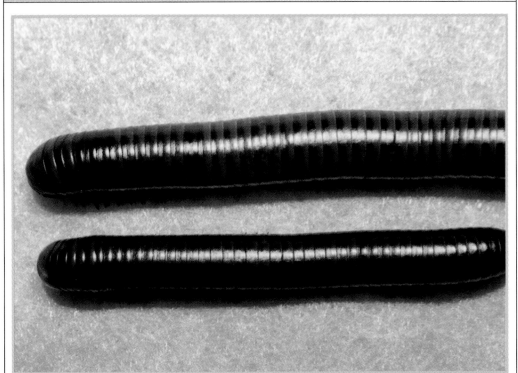

You don't always have to see gonopods or cyphopods to tell sex. Top (dorsal) and bottom (ventral) views of a *Tylobolus* species from California show some differences. Females often are thicker in diameter than males. Even when the gonopods are pulled within the body of the male, there usually is an obvious gap between the legs of segment seven lacking in the female.

Photos: M. Walls

From the side, a female (left) shows a continuous count of pairs of legs, while a male has a distinct gap where the legs are modified into gonopods.

Photo: M. Walls

millipede over and convince it to uncurl the body a bit. I find that if you take a large millipede and hold it upside-down by the tail end over your other hand, it will uncoil the front segments in an attempt to extend that extra inch to reach your hand. Count back seven rings, starting with the collum as ring or segment one. All normal male millipedes of the types you are likely to have (excluding the pill millipedes) will have modified legs on segment seven. The catch is that often the gonopods are internal except when mating. In this case you will see that the ring extends around the belly of the millipede without having any feet on it, or one pair of legs will be absent. In a female the seventh segment has two normal pairs of legs, while in males there will be one pair (not two), no obvious pairs, one normal pair plus a modified gonopod, or even two pairs of

modified gonopods. Additionally, males often have the outer angle of the jaw (the cardo) roughened and enlarged, may have the first pair of legs heavy and elongated compared to those of a female, and the seventh segment itself may be enlarged to accommodate the muscles and internal struts that help support the gonopods. In some millipedes the anterior legs of the male have obvious hairy pads that make them easy to distinguish from females.

An adult female millipede can be recognized by looking for cyphopods behind the legs on the second segment. These often are whitish and appear like small swollen mounds that often have tiny flattened flanges or serrated edges. The seventh segment will be normal, with two pairs of walking legs that look just like those in front and behind.

MATING

Sexually active millipedes seem to recognize each other by chemical senses, and it is likely that females lay down a track of sexual attractants (pheromones) to draw males. Mating is an active business in millipedes, and though females are far from passive, it is the male who does most of the chasing, catching, and positioning of the female for sex.

A male typically comes upon a female from behind and literally walks over her back, possibly licking or chewing small chemical tidbits along the way. (Many male millipedes have hairy pads on some of their anterior legs to help them walk easier on the polished back of a female.) Once his head is a few segments behind her head, the female begins to turn around or up, while the male continues to move forward, until the two animals are about face-to-face. At this point the male uses his jaws or mandibles (often enlarged, remember) to grab the female's head or perhaps the bases of her antennae. This gives him leverage to continue twisting the female around until her undersurface lies opposite his.

They end up with the second segment of the female (containing the vulvae in their cyphopods) facing the seventh segment of the male (with its modified gonopods). At this point the male extrudes several sperm packets from the penes on his second segment and begins to "walk" them down to the bases of the gonopods. There they enter the sperm ducts on the coxae and are transmitted up the ducts toward the tips of the gonopods. Probably both gonopods are used during a mating, as sperm appears in both cyphopods. Sperm may be stored for several weeks or even months, as the eggs may not be laid until the next season in some types of millipedes.

Mating pairs of millipedes may hold their positions for only a few minutes or for several hours. It is not uncommon to find mating pairs of polydesmids (the flat types) under logs and debris, and these will hold their positions even if gently handled. The large round spirobolids and spirostreptids tend to have more fleeting mating embraces and separate easily if disturbed.

EGG-LAYING

Among the larger millipedes, there are two types of egg-laying

Characteristic droppings of a large spirobolid millipede, *Chicobolus spinigerus*. Round millipedes usually place a single egg within a modified fecal ball. Such "incubators" may be almost impossible to detect when cleaning the cage.

Photo: M. Walls

practiced by females. The polydesmids have one type, the spirobolids and spirostreptids another.

Polydesmids lay small, round, white eggs in groups of 20 to hundreds. Usually the eggs are somewhat adhesive and become finely coated with soil as they are laid. They are placed in a shallow soil-covered "nest" that often is rounded or bell-shaped and develop within the chamber. Not uncommonly females stay near their eggs, but often they die after laying. Females may lay many clutches of eggs over a few weeks or months, often several months after mating takes place.

Round millipedes have a more complicated laying procedure. A female produces a special hollow pellet of fine plant debris, soil, and possibly feces by chewing the mix and manipulating it with her legs. The open pellet is brought up to the second segment, an egg is placed in it, and then the egg pellet is passed back to the anal valves, where it is inserted into the rectum. In millipedes the rectum has the ability to take up water from the substrate (some millipedes actually drink with their tails, apparently), and in this case the rectum absorbs excess water from the egg pellet before it is passed on and mixed in with the normal fecal pellets. The round millipedes produce many, many fecal pellets that are several millimeters in diameter and dark brown, usually reflecting the mix of soil and digested food that they contain. Egg pellets tend to be a bit larger than regular fecal pellets and often are paler as they dry.

Probably each species of millipede has a distinct laying season, perhaps laying only once or twice per year. *Narceus* has been recorded laying in June and August, while *Oxidus* (the greenhouse millipede) lays through much of the year if the temperature and humidity are correct.

DEVELOPMENT

Millipedes go through a long series of larval molts during which they develop an increasing number of segments and leg pairs. Development seems to be similar in both the round spirobolids and spirostreptids as well as the flat polydesmids, though the smaller number of segments in polydesmids of course leads to a shorter development period. Few species have been followed through a complete developmental cycle, and it is possible that there are many variations on the basic theme in the various families. However, the following general scheme (based on *Narceus* and *Oxidus*) is given here as a basic life cycle.

After an egg is laid it develops for probably a week or less before the first larval stage (each stage is called an instar) hatches out. The larva is tiny, white, virtually blind except for small dark eyespots, and has no distinct legs or even segments. The larva often has a great problem escaping from the egg shell, especially if the

Photo: M. Walls

A young but active *Tylobolus* larva compared to the point of a pushpin. The pale coloration is typical of most larvae.

moisture levels are unsatisfactory. In groups that produce egg pellets, the first through probably third larval instars are passed within the pellet, so their development will not be noticed in the terrarium. Polydesmids tend to pass the early stages in the nest as well and don't move into the outside world until perhaps the fourth instar.

The second instar follows within hours (to perhaps a few days) of hatching. It is similar to the first instar but usually has a distinct head and mouthparts and probably feeds for a few weeks within the pellet or nest. The third instar (following the second molt) looks like a tiny millipede with a reduced number of segments and several pairs of legs. In *Narceus* there are 21 segments at this stage and seven pairs of legs, along with three ocelli in each eye patch. The polydesmid *Oxidus gracilis*, the small hothouse millipede, has 12 segments and 11 pairs of legs at this stage by comparison. This instar may last for three weeks to a couple of months, and the larvae actively feed and move about at this time, often leaving the nest or chewing their way out of the egg pellet.

Each of the following instars adds legs and segments and feeds for several weeks before the next molt. The number of legs added obviously depends on the number in the adult, and so does the number of ocelli added to the eye patch. (Remember that most polydesmids are blind.) In *Narceus* instar four has 24 to 27 segments (much individual variation depending on growth rate) and is about 11 mm long (almost half an inch). There are three rows of eyes (ocelli) in each patch, with three eyes in the posterior row, two in the middle row, and one in the anterior row. Eye number and placement are very important to specialists following development of millipedes and often are easily seen. Instar five has 29 to 32 segments and ten eyes in each patch, while instar six has about 35 segments and 15 eyes per patch. Seventh instar *Narceus* have 21 ocelli per patch and about 40 segments. From this point on there is so much variation in growth that instar numbers mean very little. In the final molt all the posterior

A group of tiny African blacks, *Archispirostreptus* probably *gigas*, hatched and developing in a planted terrarium. Millipede breeding still is largely accidental in proper surroundings.

Photo: T. Moran

segments will bear legs except for the telson ring, and the sexual organs will be fully developed. Adult *Narceus* may continue to molt a few times after attaining sexual maturity. It may take six to eight months, possibly a full year, for the millipede to become mature, and in millipedes that live in areas with very short active seasons larval development may require several years.

In *Oxidus* there are fewer legs and segments and of course no eyes. By the fourth instar there are 15 segments, in the fifth 17 segments, in the sixth 18 (with 26 leg pairs in males and 27 in females, plus the rudiments of the male gonopods). Instar seven has 19 segments and 28 or 29 pairs of legs (male one fewer than female), and the terminal or adult instar, number eight, has 20 segments and 30 or 31 pairs of legs. Each instar lasts about four to eight weeks, the later instars differing greatly in duration due to food availability and temperature. The adult *Oxidus gracilis* is about 20 to 21 mm long, a bit less than an inch. In this species the adults live just one season and die after mating or egg-laying depending on the sex.

IN THE TERRARIUM

My limited experiences with breeding millipedes in the terrarium indicate that at least some of the females offered for sale are already fertile and will lay their eggs in the litter of the terrarium bottom. I have yet to find an egg pellet, but since young have appeared in the terrarium, they must be present. The young millipedes when first seen on the surface (usually feeding on fungus under small pieces of wood) have been only 10 mm or so long (less than half an inch) and pale creamy tan to almost white, with distinct legs and small black dots on the sides that represent the repugnatorial glands. (We'll talk about these glands later when we go over care of the species.) They are fairly inactive and do not seem to be bothered by adults in the same terrarium, even if there is little floor space. They seem to double their size in a month, but I've seen none molting. Apparently most millipede activities occur at night and under the substrate. My young so far have been too delicate to survive to adulthood or even to attain adult coloration. Maybe I'll have better luck later. (Young have been seen for *Chicobolus* and *Tylobolus*; *Orthoporus* and *Archispirostreptus* have not yet reproduced for me, though I've seen mating of *Orthoporus*.)

European myriapodologists (the study of wild millipedes is a pleasant Sunday hobby in many

The pale coloration is a good sign that this xystodesmid from Georgia still has not reached maturity though almost as long as an adult. At this stage of development the gonopods are simple and nonfunctional and color patterns are weak or absent, making identification almost impossible.

Photo: M. Smith

parts of Europe, with local clubs and yearly excursions to good collecting areas) have studied the life cycles of many of their species in great detail. They have produced charts of exact sizes (measured as diameters or widths of rings rather than total length, which can change after preservation) and eye arrangements for each instar, and also have followed the changes that occur in gonopods with growth. There are usable handbooks that allow easy identification of the millipedes of many European countries.

Unfortunately, almost no European millipedes are of interest to terrarium hobbyists, and even the millipedes of the United States are virtually unknown when it comes to the details of their life histories; even identifications are almost impossible unless you have males and identified specimens for comparison. Much remains to be learned about all the millipedes, large and small, temperate and tropical, and the hobbyist should be alert to take careful notes of anything interesting that happens.

Adult western desert millipedes, in this case *Orthoporus flavior*, might survive a decade in the wild, but they tend to be considerably shorter-lived in the terrarium. The larger millipedes of most interest to hobbyists have been poorly studied compared to many tiny species that intrigue scientists.

Photo: M. Walls

GENERAL CARE OF MILLIPEDES

When it comes to the details of caring for millipedes, you can feel free to experiment. Very little has been published on millipede care other than the "natural" system usually used in laboratory studies of millipedes. We'll discuss this method and more typical terrarium setups shortly. Different millipedes seem to have different tolerances for temperature, humidity, food, and substrates, and much of keeping currently is guesswork.

> Though the natural method of keeping works well for small to minute species of millipedes that require very constant humidity conditions, it is unsatisfactory for terrarium pets.

Photo: M. Walls

THE TERRARIUM

Two methods, the natural and the artificial, can be used to keep millipedes with some degree of confidence. Each has its advantages and disadvantages. For various reasons I am a proponent of the artificial method, but for many types of millipedes the natural method works best.

The Natural Method

For small millipedes and delicate forms, this is the only way to go. Basically, you take a large jar, preferably about a gallon (3.8 liters) or so, and fill it with leaf litter, rotting wood, and other debris from the natural habitat of the millipedes being kept. The millipedes are added (often in large numbers if you are dealing with small species) and the lid is screwed on tightly. As long as the humidity in the jar is maintained at about 100% (you may have to lightly spray the litter before closing the jar), most millipedes will do very well. They will feed on the litter and the tiny fungi growing on it and often will mate and reproduce as if they were at home. The jar should be kept in a cool, dark area, such as in a cabinet, and opened every two to four weeks to check the moisture and be sure the culture has not gone bad.

The natural secretions of the millipedes will tend to keep

excess fungi down, but sometimes things will get out of hand and the litter will have to be changed. Also, be sure that there are only millipedes in the jar, no insect larvae. Many flies and beetles will prey on millipedes and may kill off a colony. Springtails, tiny wingless insects that hop, will always develop in the culture, but they are harmless and serve as good garbage recyclers to help reduce waste matter in the jar.

If you wish, you can replace the jar with a small aquarium (1 gallon, 3.8 liters) and seal it with a piece of glass cut to size. Petroleum jelly on the frame of the terrarium will produce a good seal to keep humidity high in the terrarium.

Obviously, millipedes kept in a natural setup are not pets because the keeper has little or no interaction with his charges. If you want to keep small species, however, this may be the only way to go.

The Artificial Method

Though it has its problems and may be more stressful on the millipedes, large species will survive well in a true terrarium. Depending on the size of the millipede, glass and plastic

The terrarium for a millipede can be very simple. Often moist wood chips over a sand or soil base will suffice if cover is present as well. This *Aphistogoniulus* from Madagascar never did adapt well to either moist or dry surroundings, however.

Photo: M. Walls

aquaria and shoe boxes from 6 inches to 18 inches (150 to 461 mm) long and appropriately deep will suffice. Most millipedes will stand on the substrate and try to climb the corners of the terrarium, with only their last few segments still touching the ground. Thus for safety the depth of the terrarium should be at least 1.5 times the length of the longest millipede being kept, even taller if there are climbing branches leaning against the walls.

Many millipedes will climb freely if given the opportunity, so a few low surfaces such as branches and pieces of cork bark should be present. These also give the millipedes cover from the light.

The substrate is one of the major problems in keeping millipede terraria. I've had good luck with wood chips (preferably hardwood and never cedar, which has too many volatile oils) about 1 to 2 inches (25 to 50 mm) deep. Before adding the millipedes I cover the chips with water and allow them to soak for a day, then pour off excess water that has not been absorbed. A mixture of potting soil and sand (about 2:1) is put in one corner to serve as an area for possible egg-laying and molting cells. (Millipedes often molt in shallow depressions in soil that they cover over; molting may take several days and is a very dangerous time for a millipede.) A few pieces of soaked wood, a piece of cork bark for cover, and sometimes shallow food and water dishes complete the arrangements.

Other hobbyists have used more elaborate setups. They put a layer of small gravel down first to help absorb wastes and then cover this with a couple of inches of orchid bark, potting soil, vermiculite, and similar moisture-holding substrates. Probably almost anything that holds water and does not fungus too rapidly will work. I don't like vermiculite because when I tried to use it with *Chicobolus*, the animals immediately started eating it (vermiculite is an inert mineral with no nutritional value) and producing bright silvery fecal pellets that looked like little balls of aluminum foil. More natural setups, with moss sheets and plants, certainly will not be appreciated by the millipedes, but they do look good. Remember: The substrate may be moist but *never* wet.

You will have to maintain high humidities in the terrarium. Instead of trying to find a lid that fits perfectly, I cut a piece of heavy plastic (such as used for insulating windows during the winter) so it is an inch or so wider than the terrarium top in every direction. The regular lid for the terrarium (either mesh or slotted plastic) then simply is placed over the plastic, which seals the surface sufficiently to promote proper humidity levels.

TEMPERATURE, HUMIDITY, AND LIGHT

Millipedes, even those of the deserts, do not like it hot. Many species from the United States actually like it very cool, and almost all like humid retreats. I suggest you try for an average temperature near 75F (24C) if possible and try to hold the terraria below 86F (30C) at all times. The large desert millipedes seem to do well at these temperatures, but the litter-dwellers may be stressed at anything over 80F (27C). I lost most of my colony of *Tylobolus* when we had a two-week period of 95F (35C) weather. Putting them in a refrigerator at about 48F (9C) for a few days saved some, but all were highly stressed and stopped eating. Deep layers of damp substrate generate quite a bit of heat from natural processes, a factor that has to be remembered when determining the temperature in the terrarium. Adding an inch or so of water to a tray under the terrarium may help a culture make it through one or two exceptionally warm days if you cannot provide air conditioning.

Even desert millipedes such as *Orthoporus* like humid surroundings. During the day they are deep under cover in the most moist areas they can find, and they tend to emerge only after rains or when there is a considerable amount of morning dew. The giant African black, *Archispirostreptus* sp., seems to be comfortable at lower humidities, however. You should

Giant African blacks are voracious feeders and take a wide variety of foods, from fresh vegetables to commercial iguana food. Notice that several sizes, bred in the terrarium, are feeding from the same dish here.

By giving a variety of foods, you allow your pet to select textures and tastes most to its liking. This particular western desert millipede, *Orthoporus* probably *ornatus*, has a taste for bits of tomato and cabbage, often refusing lettuce.

Photo: M. Walls

be able to tell from their behavior if the millipedes are comfortable. If they remain tightly curled at all times, they probably are trying to conserve body water from evaporation, and the humidity should be increased. Try to spray every terrarium with lukewarm water at least twice a week.

When the temperature in the terrarium rises, humidity also rises and condensation may occur on the lid. This should be avoided. If you have a plastic sheet under a mesh or slotted lid, just pull the plastic back an inch or so to temporarily reduce the humidity and prevent condensation.

Most millipedes are nocturnal, and they actively avoid the light. Even the eyeless polydesmids can sense light and try to burrow away from it. On the other hand, many millipedes may be seasonally active during the day, especially on damp, dull days. African giant pills have been found climbing trees in full daylight, and numbers of *Narceus* and *Orthoporus* have been seen moving across roads in midmorning. If you provide the millipedes with cover to escape the light and also try to keep the terraria out of strong light, you should be fine.

Most millipedes burrow into the substrate, but the larger species tend to be active on the surface most of the time. The large species don't object violently to handling (but see the discussions of particular species). Don't drop a squirming millipede or you will risk killing it. Most weight only a few grams, however, and can survive short falls; they must often drop from low branches in nature anyway. Legs broken in normal activity or handling usually heal but don't regenerate.

FEEDING

With few exceptions, millipedes are plant-eaters. In nature they feed on coarse vegetable debris (including rotting wood), fungi, and perhaps algae from lichens. Occasionally they take living plants such as potatoes, and some will feed on dead insects. They are one group of animals that finds lettuce a decent food, but even they won't eat the white stems of iceberg lettuce. A mixture of leaf lettuce, tomato cores and fleshy peelings, apple bits, squashed green peas, and almost any other firm vegetable or fruit will be eaten. (These and similar moist foods may fungus overnight in the terrarium, causing bad smells and requiring constant cleaning.) Iguana and turtle pellets also can be tried, as can small bits of moist dogfood treats. Many small litter-dwellers will not eat lettuce at all and seldom eat other foods provided on the surface of the terrarium. You have to give them fresh leaf litter every month or so or they

In nature millipedes usually feed off the substrate or just below its surface, but in the terrarium it is easier to use small lids as feeding dishes, keeping the bottom more sanitary and less subject to fungus. Fungus may be the keeper's number one problem.

Photo: M. Walls

Many African blacks are literally crawling with commensal mites. These often scuttle about just over the bases of the legs, feeding on bits of food and probably feces. Though harmless, some hobbyists find them distasteful on their pets and try unsuccessfully to remove them.

will starve.

The large millipedes will take their food scattered on the surface of the terrarium or in a shallow bowl (preferred). African blacks are voracious eaters, as are most of the other large round millipedes. Polydesmids eat mostly litter. Almost any millipede will eat apple, by the way, and some keepers find the same with corn on the cob. I find that millipedes eat less when the temperature rises above 86F (30C) and as the autumn approaches.

The terrarium must be cleaned at least twice weekly, when the millipedes are fed. I usually go in, remove excessive amounts of fecal pellets with a spoon (you might want to hold these pellets aside for about a month to be sure you are not throwing away egg pellets as well), take out any leftover food bits, clean or replace the dish, check to make sure all specimens still look healthy and active (or remove dead bodies if necessary, putting them directly into alcohol), and put in the fresh food. Before closing the lid, I spray the bottom and sides of the terrarium with dechlorinated water. This operation is repeated every three days or so.

Many larger millipedes will actively drink water from a small dish, but others won't. I've yet to be able to tell if this is a species character or an individual trait. It won't hurt to put a bottle cap of fresh water in the terrarium each time you feed.

It has been suggested that many millipedes need mineral supplements. A few keepers add a dish of calcium powder to the terrarium, add calcium to the food, or sprinkle calcium on the substrate every month. Use reptile calcium supplements available in pet shops or small bits of cuttlebone. Certainly extra calcium won't hurt, because millipedes lose a great deal of calcium when they molt (although they eat their shed skins and recapture at least some of the calcium that way).

COMMENSALS

Large round millipedes may support populations of small, very active mites that belong to the gamasid group. Species of the genera *Neomegistus* and *Paramegistus* have been identified on the African blacks, and similar mites are common on *Narceus*. These mites are commensals, free-living forms that use the millipedes as places to live and possibly feed on food fragments from the millipede's meals. They tend to be tan to reddish in color and are very active on the lower body of the millipede above the bases of the legs. They are harmless and probably impossible to remove—anything that kills them probably would kill the millipede as well. If they really annoy you, try washing them off with warm water or picking them off with a damp brush. Preserved specimens might be of interest to mite specialists, as I am sure there are many undescribed species out there.

Springtails, Collembola, a group

This ***Orthoporus ornatus*** clearly shows the openings to the repugnatorial glands outlined in black on the lower sides. The glands themselves secrete a mixed brew of chemicals that in nature probably help chase off ants and other small but determined predators.

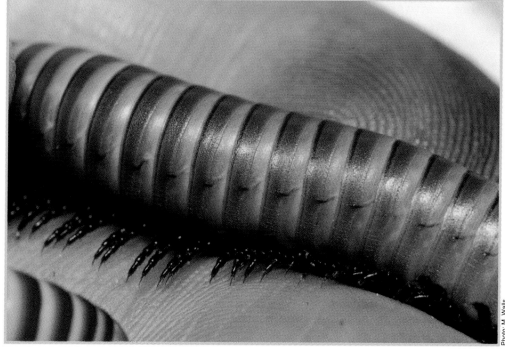

Photo: M. Walls

of primitive wingless insects, always appear in millipede cultures and are harmless. They help control fungus and bacteria in the culture. More harmful are the small flies, some at least belonging to the family Phoridae, that appear in some cultures. These flies lay eggs on the millipedes and produce larvae that may kill a small millipede.

REPUGNATORIAL PORES

Millipedes can produce a regular stew of volatile chemicals that they use to ward off predators and perhaps control fungal growth in the leaf litter. The chemicals are released through small pores, often black or outlined in a contrasting color, on the sides of the body, usually one pair of pores per segment. Not every segment has a pore, and different families of millipedes have pores on specific segments and lack them on others. These pores are known as repugnatorial pores or ozopores and the chemicals technically are allomones. In some tropical millipedes the chemicals can be ejected under pressure and sprayed several inches, preferably into the eyes of the shrew or mouse that is trying to dine on the millipede; it can cause temporary blindness in a small mammal. In the flattened polydesmids the principal ingredient is hydrogen cyanide (prussic acid, cyanide) with some benzaldehyde. Polydesmids that are picked up thus smell like cherry or bitter almond. Spirobolids produce a family of

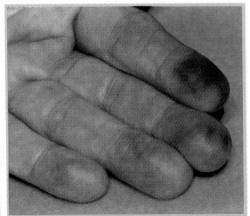

The red-stained fingers of a millipede keeper and a distinctive iodine-like smell are just part of the hobby. Several of the chemicals secreted by millipedes may be nauseating if swallowed, and they can damage clothing, but millipedes are not considered to be especially toxic or dangerous animals.

Photo: M. Walls

chemicals known as quinones that can cause chemical burns on delicate tissue, while spirostreptids produce mostly benzoquinones.

All the larger millipedes will stain your hands a rich reddish brown, but the chemical is harmless to animals our size unless you foolishly rub it into your eyes, nose, or mouth. It does not wash off, burning the top layer of skin much like an iodine burn, and may take several days to wear off. If you get it on your clothes, it may stain permanently and also weaken the fabric. Use some caution when handling a large millipede but don't worry about their chemicals too much. Oh yes—never cage another animal with a millipede, especially a polydesmid, as it will die from concentrations of the chemical in the air of the terrarium. The chemicals all have strong odors that may take some getting used to.

SOME LITTLE GUYS

Of the well over 6,000 species of millipedes described, most are small. Only a few are large enough to appeal to most hobbyists and be commercially collected for the terrarium trade. However, this does not mean that the smaller millipedes are without interest to keepers. Though your contact with them cannot be as direct as with larger forms, they may be attractive to the eye and have fascinating habits.

Most small millipedes (under 2 inches, 50 mm) are best kept in a natural terrarium with leaf litter from their natural habitat. Most desiccate easily if the humidity drops, but some are quite tolerant of drier conditions. Often it is impossible to know what conditions to give a strange millipede, so you might have to provide both moist and dry conditions in a small terrarium and see which the millipede prefers. Never let a millipede desiccate, however.

The following discussions of a few smaller millipedes are meant to give you a glimpse of the diversity of types to be found even among the North American fauna. Millipedes of similar types are

Though seldom reaching an inch in length, the pink *Brachycybe* species are real eye-catchers both in nature and the terrarium. Their very flattened form and elaborate sculpture (visible with magnification) give them a unique appearance.

In nature, *Brachycybe* specimens often are found in large groups of various sizes under decaying oak logs. Immatures remain with their parents and may be protected by them until fully grown, resulting in distinctive colonies. This is an ancient genus found not only in the southern U.S. and along the Pacific Coast but also in Japan.

Photo of Tennessee specimens: P. Freed

found almost around the globe, and a couple of the types mentioned below actually have been introduced around the world.

BRACHYCYBE

These little pink millipedes are real eye-catchers even though they are only half an inch to an inch (12 to 25 mm) long. They are flattened, very broad, and have wide segments with projecting paranota. The anterior paranota curve forward to almost hide the head from view from above, and the posterior paranota do the same backward. Under magnification it can be seen that the segments are covered with rows of tiny tubercles. The legs and gonopods are rather simple. They are members of the family Andrognathidae, order Platydesmida, and are found in the southeastern United States, California, and Japan, indicating an old group that has been around for millions of years.

Pinkies are associated with decaying damp wood and leaves, especially oak. They may be found by turning rotting oak logs and looking at the surface in contact with the soil, plus the top inch or so of soil under the log. Often colonial, when you find one specimen you may find dozens of all ages and sizes. Specimens often are arranged in a "star cluster," the bodies seeming to radiate from a common center, all the animals pointing at the center. Their natural history is poorly known, but it appears that a female lays clusters of 30 to 75 or so tiny white eggs and then leaves them to the care of the male. The male circles around the eggs and guards them for the month or so that it takes before hatching. A guarding male sometimes presents the appearance of a tiny pink picket fence as the tips of the segments can be seen projecting vertically. The larvae appear to undergo about six or seven instars before becoming mature.

Adult *Brachycybe* commonly have more than 50 segments. They can move very rapidly when disturbed. Adults may live more than one year, especially since in some areas they disappear below the surface during the hot, dry months of the year, resurfacing in the autumn.

Pinkies are best kept in small sealed jars of litter and rotting oak wood on which they were collected, but they will survive for at least a while in a small terrarium as well if the humidity stays high. Though they are small, I feel they are among the most beautiful of the millipedes.

ABACION

Not all millipedes are slow plodders or inactive burrowers in the soil. The several species of *Abacion* found in the eastern United States, plus the many similar genera of the western United States, are fairly large (2 inches, 50 mm), slender, cylindrical millipedes that are covered with many ridges or crests on each segment. The arrangement and number of the crests vary from genus to genus, but the overall dark brown, nearly black, color and cresting give the millipedes a very velvety look, so I like to call the group the velvet millipedes. *Abacion* is placed in the family Caspiopetalidae and subfamily Abacioninae, while most of the western genera are in the related family Schizopetalidae, though their relationships really are in doubt.

A velvet in motion is true natural beauty. They seem to literally flow from place to place, though you can see that small groups of legs are moved in sequence. The antennae are very long, slender, and very mobile, and the millipedes give the impression of predators in search of prey. Actually, they eat leaf litter like other small millipedes, but they also are not averse to scavenging on dead crickets or flies on occasion. They prefer drier habitats than many other millipedes and often are found in sandy pine forests under pine needles. When kept at higher humidities they become sluggish and die in a few weeks. They appear to sip water from moistened paper towels.

There are many crested millipedes around the world, but most are tiny and probably impossible to keep without difficulty. Some Asian crested

Velvet millipedes are distinctive in shape and behavior from most other common millipedes. Their loosely articulated bodies and long legs let the millipedes move swiftly, the crests probably defend from attacks by ants, and the millipedes do best under relatively dry conditions. Few other millipedes have been reported feeding on dead (or disabled) insects and scraps of animal protein.

Photos: M. Smith (on leaf) and M. Walls

millipedes have very high crests and reach moderate sizes, so they might make good terrarium animals if available. Tropical millipedes often tend to develop crests and spines that perhaps help protect them from attacks by ants as well as camouflaging their body form and making it harder to see them.

JULIDS

The wireworm millipedes of the order Julida are a diverse group of poorly understood slender, cylindrical forms that look like tiny spirobolids at first glance. Though several families are found mostly in North America (including the Paeromopodidae and Parajulidae), the most commonly seen types are members of the families Julidae and Blaniulidae, introduced around the world from Europe, Africa, and perhaps Asia in the rootballs of trees and potted plants. No matter where you go in the eastern United States, for instance, you are likely to find small species of *Proteroiulus, Brachyiulus, Nopoiulus, Choneiulus,* and *Boreoiulus* whenever you sift

Oxidus gracilis **is one of the most easily observed smaller millipedes in the U.S. Once noticed, their shape (like brown-edged black beads on a string) and distinctive smell make them easy to recognize.**

Photo: M. Walls

through the leaf litter or turn bits of trash, even in your back yard.

Julids are the dominant round millipedes of Europe, and they are very well-studied there. Details of their life history are readily available in handbooks and detailed reference works. They are very important in decomposing leaf litter and may occur by the millions in small areas of pasture and forest. They also are almost the only millipedes that will attack living plants, having been known to damage crops of potatoes and other root vegetables. Most are under an inch in length, brownish, and sometimes intricately patterned if you look at them through a microscope.

The North American endemic (found nowhere else, until introduced by man) *Nopoiulus minutus* (now placed in a separate genus by some workers) is parthenogenetic, males being almost unknown, while the Old World *N. kochi* has normal sex ratios and functional males. Both are common in the eastern United States. In species of related genera some populations may be parthenogenetic, others normally sexual. Identification of these millipedes is hard, and the tiny size of the gonopods makes it difficult to observe the details of their structure. The different families and genera differ in details of the eye patches, presence or absence of a spine on the telson ring, number and length of setae or hairs on the body, and sometimes color pattern. *Proteroiulus fuscus*, for instance, has a large deep brown spot on each segment, while *Brachyiulus lusitanus* has two narrow yellow stripes down the back with an even narrower dark line within. Many species will feed on potatoes and old carrots in captivity.

OXIDUS

The greenhouse millipede, *Oxidus gracilis*, of the gigantic Asian family Paradoxosomatidae, is a small, flat polydesmid millipede that is readily recognized by appearance and habitat. Adults are less than an inch (about 20 to 22 mm) long and have rounded paranota. They are deep brown to almost black, very polished and shiny, with the legs, ventral surfaces, and edges of the paranota paler translucent brown. Each segment has a deep groove across the middle from side to side. Subadults are creamy white. These are millipedes that are strongly associated with man and have been introduced around the world in warmer climates. Additionally, they seem to adapt gradually to

cooler climes and eventually move from the warm greenhouse to debris near the warm basements of northern homes, even being able to in some cases exist far from sources of warmth in the northeastern United States and Europe. Like other man-loving millipedes (technically called synanthropes) they now are found almost everywhere. Other paradoxosomatids are large and often colorful tropical species that might make good terrarium inhabitants but never are imported.

Oxidus, as we have seen, has been fairly well studied and its life history is known. For a small millipede it can be very conspicuous, as it lives under debris rather than deep in the leaf litter. It also can be amazingly abundant in an area and occasionally has migrations when thousands or perhaps millions will just get up and move to a new area for unknown reasons. I've seen thousands littering the banks of a small New Jersey stream where a migration seemed to have ended its trek by entering the water and drowning. I've also seem them coming under the outside office doors at T.F.H. in large numbers. Like many other polydesmids, they produce a hydrocyanic acid fluid from the repugnatorial glands on the sides of the paranota. This smelly fluid stains the fingers reddish brown and is harmless to man (though extremely bitter) but probably defends the millipedes from ants and other deadly tiny predators. *Oxidus* is amazingly tolerant to water and has been noted to survive total immersion for at least seven days. Yes, I know this seems in conflict with my story above of finding thousands drowned in a local stream. Research on other species, including a Brazilian millipede that can survive the annual flooding of the Amazon each year (surviving for several months under 50 feet, 15 meters, of water), indicates that the millipedes need a period of hours to adjust to immersion; perhaps my hapless migrants just fell in and never had a chance to adapt.

At any time of the year many or most of the greenhouse millipedes will be mating pairs. These millipedes stay attached for hours and perhaps days at a time. Adult males die after mating (which may have something to do with their reluctance to release the female—just kidding) and females die after laying their eggs.

XYSTODESMIDS, EURYURIDS, AND OTHER POLYDESMIDS

The most colorful millipedes in North America are small to moderate in size (usually under 2 inches, 50 mm), flattened with large paranota, and virtually unseen unless you collect them yourself. The eastern United States and the West Coast have a large fauna of polydesmids belonging to the family Xystodesmidae, a group also represented in Mexico and China (among other areas). They can be recognized in a general way by the telson being drawn out into a short, heavy point and by their generally polished appearance. Most are found in the mountains, from the Ozarks to the Appalachians and also the Sierras of California and the Pacific Northwest, where they prefer humid habitats in litter and under logs. Females of most species and genera are practically

The color pattern and modified telson spine show this colorful Georgia millipede to be a euryurid, family Platyrhacidae. Unfortunately, the two common eastern U.S. genera, *Auturus* and *Euryurus*, are not distinguishable without examination of the gonopods under magnification.

Photo: M. Smith

Two colorful xystodesmid millipedes from Tennessee (yellow spots) and Georgia (red bands). Without looking at gonopods, identification is almost impossible, but the yellow-spotted one may be a *Pachydesmus*, the red-banded specimen an *Apheloria*. Xystodesmidae includes some of the most colorful and keepable millipedes in the U.S., though adults do tend to die after breeding.

Photos: M. Smith

identical, and you often cannot even guess the genus unless you have a male with distinctive and highly modified gonopods. They have only a single pair of gonopods, the legs at the front of the seventh segment. Over 50 genera and multitudes of species (many undescribed) occur in the United States, with more south of the border.

The attractions of these millipedes are their broadly flattened form and bright colors. Even a specimen only an inch (25 mm) long looks impressive against the litter when you see the shiny black or deep brown body marked with bright red or yellow spots

The broad paranota and (under magnification) delicate sculpturing of the rings help identify this small New Jersey millipede as a native *Pseudopolydesmus* species. In back yards under trash one often finds similar (but rougher) introduced species of *Polydesmus* and allied genera.

Photo: M. Walls

and bands. The color patterns often are shared by several unrelated species in one area, while a single species may show several different colors and patterns in a single area. The purpose of the brilliant colors is uncertain, as these are eyeless millipedes active mostly at night in full darkness when they come out of the litter. The larvae are white or pale pinkish. Like other polydesmids, most adults die after mating and producing eggs. The larvae take about a year to mature. Keep them cool (preferably under 70F, 21C) and in deep leaf litter if you want to try to keep them.

Very similar at first glance to the xystodesmids are the somewhat more slender and typically smaller euryurids. These polydesmids belong to the family Platyrhacidae (formerly they were a full family, Euryuridae, thus the common name) and are easily recognized in the United States by the their distinctive telson spine, which is squared off at the tip and a bit wider at the tip than the base, much like a fingernail. They also have a distinctive color pattern with a wide triangular yellow or red spot on the outer edges of the paranota (often connected to the spot on the next segment) and a triangular yellowish to reddish spot at the center back of each segment, often weakly outlined with black. The common genera, *Auturus* and *Euryurus*, are practically identical externally and must be distinguished by the gonopods. In the American tropics these may be very large and colorful millipedes that might make good terrarium inhabitants if imported. The 4-inch (100-mm) yellow and brown *Nyssodesmus python* of Caribbean Costa Rica, for instance, usually is found in sexual pairs, the male riding the back of the larger female.

An *Auturus* from central Louisiana has bred for me, producing multitudes of tiny white young that closely resemble the adults in form. Few survived more than a few months, and I am not sure what they were feeding upon. Attempts to transfer some of the young to new containers failed, while the young retained with the adults (which survived mating and egg-laying for several months) did better. The adults were noted "sitting" on top of clumps of young, which makes me suspect that there is some type of parental care involved here.

We'll close this section on little guys with a brief mention of the true polydesmids of the family Polydesmidae. These are small (an inch or less), very flat brownish millipedes. Though a few are black and some have reddish tinges, most are admittedly dull— unless you look at the sculpture of the segments under a microscope. There you will see that there are several rows of squarish indentations on the back and often tiny spines or serrations on the edges of the paranota. As usual, identification is by means of gonopods. The European genus *Polydesmus* has been widely introduced around the world with plants and is common in the northeastern United States. The slightly larger and a bit more colorful (likely to be tinged with red) genus *Pseudopolydesmus* is endemic to the eastern United States and common in the forests of the Southeast.

Unlike many millipedes, these overwinter as adults. The eggs are laid in the early summer or spring, a female producing 400 or more tiny eggs that are placed in a mud nest that looks a bit like a tiny igloo. There the larvae develop deep in the leaf litter, coming to the surface when they have become late larval instars. The late instars molt in small mud igloos like those constructed by the female for egg-laying. The larvae overwinter and only become mature during the second autumn following the laying of the eggs. Adults appear about September, but these adults again overwinter in the leaf litter until the following spring. Mating occurs both in the autumn before overwintering and in the spring following emergence. Adults die during the summer after the eggs are laid.

This very small selection of little guys of course does not even begin to mention the diversity of millipedes. I've mentioned mostly northern forms, but the poorly known tropical types are even more diverse and often strangely beautiful. Remember to keep careful notes if you try to keep any of your local little guys and preserve the bodies of those that die so they can be accurately identified.

BIG ROUND ONES

If you keep a millipede, you probably have one of the giant forms (anything from 4 inches, 100 mm, and up). These are the types that most commonly are sold in pet shops and draw the most attention. After all, when you see a shiny blackish brown millipede with dozens of red legs and it is 10 inches (250 mm) long and almost an inch in diameter, you just have to stop and look.

Unfortunately, I cannot provide a really complete treatment of the giant millipedes, because I have no idea what importers will put on the market next. Millipedes are not yet heavily commercialized animals, and the tendency is to ship whatever is big and available and get the few dollars that anything large will bring. Over the years many different millipedes have reached the terrarium hobby, but none have really lasted for more than a few years. Dealers and collectors move on to other areas and other animals, and what was common last year may be completely unavailable next year. Additionally, identification of tropical millipedes may be impossible unless specimens of males have been preserved, preferably with accurate locality data, both factors unlikely to occur.

For these reasons I will try to cover only six or seven large millipedes, all members of the spirobolid and spirostreptid groups. Both these types are cylindrical millipedes with well over 40 rings in the adult. In spirobolids (here the families Spirobolidae, Atopetholidae, and Pachybolidae) the mentum of the gnathochilarium is triangular and divides the small lingual lamina, and the eyes are in large, usually round patches. Spirostreptids (here the family Spirostreptidae and close relatives) have a more rectangular mentum with larger lingual lamina that typically are in contact, and the eyes commonly are in a narrow, curved semicircle. Please do not accept any of the identifications I use here as gospel. I've seen males of none of the imported giants, so the identifications are educated guesses based on the literature. New imports, such as the African "pumpkin" millipede, an orange-brown species with a distinctly narrower anterior body, also appear without warning.

SPIROSTREPTIDS

The **giant African millipedes**, various species of *Archispirostreptus* and probably allied genera, currently are the biggest millipedes available in the U.S. They also are among the largest in the world, with individuals often reaching 10 inches (250 mm) in total length and a few specimens reaching or exceeding a foot (300 mm). When this great length is combined with a bulky, nearly cylindrical body about an inch (25 mm) in diameter, you have a true conversation piece. Two types, assumedly species, were widely available recently. The common type (at least in eastern U.S. shops) is a deep brown, virtually black, with rosy legs. This often is called the African black. A second type is a pale caramel brown in color with tan or red legs (perhaps each leg color representing a different species again). Both come from Africa, perhaps Kenya and Tanzania, and represent a

large genus of about 15 species found in dry regions of eastern Africa to the Middle East (including Israel), with some ranging west to Senegal. The genus *Graphidostreptus* currently is treated as a synonym of *Archispirostreptus*; the related *Alloporus* (with *Doratogonus* as a synonym) occurs in southern Africa. Technical characters for distinguishing genera and species lie, as usual, in the gonopods. So far I've seen no males, and there are indications in the literature that in some species females greatly outnumber males and thus are the most likely sex to be collected and shipped.

These millipedes can be kept in

Giant African black millipedes, *Archispirostreptus* perhaps *gigas,* are the most commonly sold millipedes today, and at 8 to over 10 inches they are a true handful. Easy to keep and inexpensive, they are a good value for the terrarium hobbyist.

Photo: M. Walls

Photo: W. P. Mara

Also commonly seen is a brighter tan to reddish brown *Archispirostreptus* of uncertain status. These African browns probably represent a distinct species, but fortunately they can be kept much like African blacks.

a roomy terrarium (5 to 10 gallons, 19 to 38 liters) that is high and has a lid that attaches securely. They like to climb, and if given the chance to reach the top will almost certainly be able to push the lid off even if you clamp it down well. The substrate can be sand or wood chips, but keep it rather dry; these species don't need high humidities. Provide a water bowl (they sometimes drink) and spray them and their terrarium twice a week. African giants eat prodigious quantities of lettuce, tomatoes, cucumbers, and almost any other plant matter. My specimens, unlike other millipedes, never produced typical fecal pellets, instead producing a tar-like loose feces that stuck to the sides of the terrarium and had to be scraped off once it dried. Perhaps the foods I've given them contain more water than their intestines can deal with, but as long as they were eating I was afraid to experiment. I never noticed them burrowing into the substrate or hiding under the pieces of cork bark, but if they were allowed to dry I suspect they would try to burrow under cover looking for moist surroundings. For detailed coverage of a more natural terrarium setup, see the article by Theresa Moran in *Reptile Hobbyist*, 2(8), April, 1997.

These millipedes are always covered with small mites, which are harmless but annoying to watch. I always feel "itchy" after handling my specimens, even though I've never seen a mite actually leave a millipede's body.

African giants are fun to handle. They are a real handful, are very powerful (almost like a snake), and when unaccustomed to you will produce large amounts of secretions that will heavily stain your fingers. I had one pry the lid off its terrarium and drop 4 feet to the floor, then walk off uninjured. (Other hobbyists have reported falls leading to death, however.) So far I've seen no young, but my specimens were all females (and the couple of dozen I've examined lately also have been females) and apparently were not carrying fertile eggs. They have bred for other keepers. These may be long-lived millipedes, the larvae taking three to nine years to reach maturity and the adults probably living for several years. However, they may need a dry resting period in order to attain old age.

Western desert millipedes, *Orthoporus*, are represented by three externally identical species in the southwestern U.S.; this one is *O. ornatus*, which has the widest range. Colorful, easy to care for, and inexpensive, these 6- to 8-inch millipedes make excellent pets.

Photo: M. Walls

Much of the life of *Orthoporus ornatus* is passed inactive underground or in old rodent burrows, but this is a long-lived species in nature. In captivity it may have to be provided with wet and dry seasons (or cool and warm) to prosper.

Photo: M. Walls

The pale brown form (species, assumedly) can be very attractive and might be preferred in the eyes of many hobbyists over the black type. It is not impossible that only one species is represented, the differences in color representing seasonal variations. Specimens as small as 5 inches (125 mm) are seen at the same time as 10-inch (250-mm) giants; these may be subadults or stunted adults.

During the summer in the United States you will see many **western desert millipedes** offered for sale, and some certainly are shipped out of the country. These are relatively slender (about 0.25 to 0.5 inch, 6 to 12 mm, in diameter), long (6 to 8 inches, 150 to 200 mm), tan to bright yellow millipedes of the genus *Orthoporus*. This is a gigantic genus that ranges from Nevada to Texas and then south to Brazil; there are dozens of named species, but perhaps only 50 or so are valid. They tend to like dry habitats (but in the tropics are not averse to moist areas as well) and are most abundant, at least in the United States, after the summer rains moisten and cool the deserts. The rest of the year they burrow under rocks or hide in deep crevices in the soil, perhaps going down as much as 30 inches (760 mm) to seek shelter from the heat. They are active on cool, cloudy days and at night, and they often cross highways in large numbers. I found them quite common in late May in southern Texas, collecting two putative species during a long drive between Big Bend and Del Rio.

The species of *Orthoporus* are notoriously difficult to distinguish, and males are uncommon, being greatly outnumbered by females and subadults. The species are quite variable in details of shape and coloration, though the U.S. species tend to be ringed in darker brown and yellowish brown (but nearly black, reddish, and nearly yellow individuals occur in the same collections). At least in captivity, it seems that individuals tend to become paler (more yellow, less brown) as the year progresses, specimens that were dull tan and blackish tan in May becoming bright yellow and reddish tan by September. They are active, fast-moving millipedes that actually seem to survive to get to the other side of the road. Their preferred habitats range from dry prairie to true desert. They are adapted to prevent water loss by having a very waxy outer covering on the body and survive by feeding on very low grade, coarse vegetation, including rotting wood.

Adults mate and lay eggs after the rains let them resume activity (often late May to early June). Females deposit from 50 to 500 egg pellets in an underground chamber in packrat burrows and under rocks. The eggs hatch in about one week, the larva remaining inside the pellet and using it for its first food. Early larvae probably overwinter as the second instar (the data are very confused and there is a tremendous amount of variation reported), and then molt again the next year when rains return. They still feed on the original egg pellet but break out when rains soak down to their level and moisten the pellet. It is not certain how many more molts the larvae go through after emerging from the pellet, but the onset of maturity probably takes several years of alternating feeding during the rainy season and being inactive in the soil during the rest of the year. When adults finally emerge (at an age of between three and six years?), they mate and lay eggs before again going into the soil. It is not known how long adults live, but they should be able to last two or three rainy seasons.

This alternation of active and inactive seasons may make these millipedes difficult to maintain. I know that my specimens slow down and almost stop eating when September comes, and I suspect they want to burrow and become inactive until next spring. I've given them a deeper substrate and hiding spots, but it is unlikely that I can duplicate their natural cycle in my animal room. Though these species can survive high temperatures for short periods, they prefer it cool and moist,

Photo: M. Walls

Florida ivory millipedes, *Chicobolus spinigerus*, are common in the southeastern U.S. and occasionally make it to the shops. The pale triangles often are strongly tinted with rose at their lower edges, giving the millipedes a distinctive appearance.

about 75 to 86F (24 to 30C). Spray the terrarium twice a week and also give them a drinking bowl. They can go through tremendous amounts of lettuce and produce gigantic piles of fecal pellets in a short period. When not feeding they tend to seek cover, many specimens entwining under a piece of cork bark or burrowing into a dark corner of the terrarium. They are quite social animals, very good climbers, and produce a great tingling feeling when walking over your hands. They can stand almost on their anal valves to try to climb the corners of the terrarium, and in nature they often are found on branches of low shrubs. By the way, this is one of the species that can drink through the anal valves, absorbing water through the walls of the rectum.

I've seen captive mating in *Orthoporus ornatus* from north of Big Bend National Park. In June the largest specimen, a nearly black male (though gonopods had not been visible externally) pinned down a smaller yellow female, threw a loop of his body around hers, and used his mandibles to hold her head in position below his. The pair mated vertically, supported by the corner of the terrarium, the legs in constant motion. At least two copulations were seen, but the couple broke up immediately when I approached them. No eggs were laid that I could detect, but this is one of those species where it may be best to hold the discarded substrate and fecal pellets for several months in case eggs are present.

I would rate these millipedes as excellent pets, especially if they can be made to survive a winter period of inactivity. Dr. C. S. Crawford, formerly of the University of New Mexico, has published many papers on the biology and physiology of this genus, including a summary paper on desert millipedes in *Zool. J. Linnean Soc.*, 89: 63-88 (1987), with other summaries on *Archispirostreptus* and the Indian *Harpagophora* by K. Bercovitz and M. R. Warburg. The paper is quite technical but has a good bibliography.

SPIROBOLOIDS

In the United States, the large millipedes of the genus *Chicobolus* (**Florida ivory**), *Narceus* (**eastern giants**), and *Tylobolus* (**California giants**), all members of the family Spirobolidae, are fairly easy to obtain during the spring and summer. All are about 4 inches (100 mm) long, rather slender, with brown to reddish brown rings and paler (red to cream) posterior portions of each ring.

In *Chicobolus spinigerus* from Florida and the southeastern U.S. the pale pattern may take the form of large triangles on each ring, giving an appearance of jagged gray-brown and white or rosy sawteeth when the millipede coils. My specimens reproduced in the terrarium. For more information on *Chicobolus*, try my article in *Reptile Hobbyist*, 1(1), September/October, 1995. The other common Florida

The only "giant" millipede likely to be collected in most of the U.S. east of the Great Plains is *Narceus americanus*, which often reaches about 5 inches in length. The thick body shape, bright pink to red edges of the black to gray rings, and pink legs make it easy to recognize.

Photo: M. Smith

Photo: M. Walls

Several genera of millipedes from the Pacific Northwest and California might be called near-giants. This *Tylobolus* from northern California is thick-bodied and colorful but tops out at under 4 inches.

spirobolid, *Narceus gordanus*, lives in sandy soils and is banded in deep brown and pale red much like the more widely distributed *Narceus americanus*, which is *the* giant millipede over most of the United States east of the Great Plains.

Narceus americanus (and its more southern subspecies *annularis*) is a 4- to 5-inch (100- to 125-mm) millipede of rather stout shape; it is dark brown with a narrow reddish ring at the back of each segment, and has pinkish legs. This species is common from the eastern Canadian border south to northern Florida (with scattered occurrences over the rest of Florida) and west to eastern Texas. In most of the eastern U.S. and Canada, this is the only truly "giant" millipede. Though its life history is fairly well-known (it forms the basis for much of the discussion in the sex and growth chapter), there still are many details to be unraveled.

It seems that adults probably live several years, emerging in spring to mate and lay eggs, disappearing during the warm, dry summer months, and returning to the surface in autumn to lay again before disappearing into the soil and rotting wood for the winter. This is a species of rotting, rather wet tree trunks on the ground and peeling bark on dead trees. It is not uncommon to find specimens climbing trees at night or crossing roads and sidewalks by the hundreds during the summer. It makes a great, easy to keep pet, but it goes through a lot of food and produces a lot of waste, making it a rather nasty species to clean up after. In the older literature, including biology texts, *Narceus americanus* was known as *Spirobolus* or *Arctobolus marginatus*.

The western American *Tylobolus* looks a lot like a *Narceus* but is a bit smaller, glossier, and tends more toward the reddish side than the brown side. The species inhabit deep leaf litter deposits over much of California and are very hard to tell apart. I've had poor luck with these millipedes because they seem unable to take the heat and humidity of a New Jersey summer when kept in a terrarium. I lost a colony of more than 40 specimens over two months when the temperature went above 86F (30C) for long periods. They did, however, reproduce in the terrarium, but the larvae were very fragile and did not survive for long. Unlike *Narceus* and *Chicobolus*, which feed on many types of vegetables and fruits, these *Tylobolus* accepted only bits of apple and never fed well. I've been told they like corn on the cob, but mine were reluctant to take this, perhaps because of heat stress. They did seem to drink a bit, however. This might be a good genus to try with a natural method setup kept in a permanently cool, dark spot.

The rather small, deep gray atopetholids of Texas and the Southwest resemble *Narceus* in some respects but have segment two ending in a point and shorter than the collum when looked at from the side. The several genera are poorly understood. They are not uncommon under rocks and debris in southern Texas, but I had very poor luck with the ones I kept for about six weeks, as both adults and juveniles died suddenly. They never fed well on the foods offered and spent most of their time coiled up under damp moss. When handled, the adults became frenzied, throwing the body in sharp, hard curves and literally leaping about in the hand, a very distinctive behavior.

The other North American spiroboloid family is represented by a single genus and species endemic to the sand flats of Florida around Lake Placid. This

This unidentified atopetholid millipede from southern Texas had attractive grayish tones and was over 3 inches long, but it proved impossible to keep for more than a few weeks. The second ring is reduced in size in these millipedes.

Photo: M. Walls

is *Floridobolus penneri*, discovered less than 50 years ago and still poorly known. It is a very chubby species much like *Narceus* at first glance but with very short legs. It is at least partially protected by Florida.

Occasional imports of the so-called **Madagascan giants** or **Madagascan reds** and **blacks** have occurred recently. These millipedes (there certainly are several species) have round eye patches and probably belong to the genus *Aphistogoniulus* of the spirobolid family Pachybolidae. The ones I've seen have been only 3 to 5 inches (75 to 125 mm) long, but supposedly they reach 8 inches (200 mm). They are black with red heads and anal segments. Some have bright red spots on the rings and/or a red stripe down the middle of the back. The legs are bright red. I've only kept the form with red head and tail and black body, and not very successfully. Though it eventually ate well and drank deeply from a bottle cap of fresh water, it never seemed comfortable. If kept in humid surroundings it curled up and became very inactive, so it was transferred to a sand base with moist woodchips in one corner of the terrarium. It then seemed considerably more comfortable and became active, usually in the drier areas of the terrarium. A lot of its time was spent coiled and inactive under cork bark, often with the legs firmly gripping the bark, the millipede thus hanging upside down. Perhaps it is a climbing species in nature, but it never seemed more arboreal that other millipedes being kept. It also did not eat for several weeks after purchase, though it finally began to take squashed green peas and

Several colors of "giant" millipedes (actually usually under 5 inches) are imported from Madagascar, and most probably belong to *Aphistogoniulus*, family Pachybolidae. This particular specimen is mostly red above, but others (species?) may be almost all black.

Photo: R. D. Bartlett

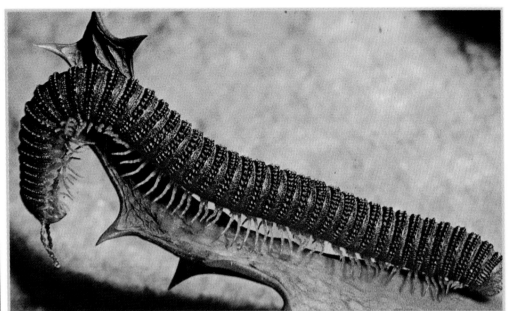

Eight-inch, heavily crested millipedes appeared in the hobby in the 1960's and 70's, supposedly imported from the Congo. Today these incredible animals are represented by just memories and a few photos. This probably was a male, as legs seem to be absent from segment seven.

apple. For some reason its food always fungused after just one day and had to be removed or replaced. Madagascar has a variety of natural habitats, from desert to rain forests, lowlands to mountains, and without knowing the origin of an import it may be difficult to acclimate it to the terrarium.

Also in the family Pachybolidae are the brilliant waxy red South African species of *Centrobolus*, better known as *Chersastus* in the literature. These are large, cylindrical species that climb well and are very active. Different species vary from almost solid red to yellow, with or without black spots. These (or a similar type of millipede) once were imported and supposedly made fine pets, but they do not appear to be available currently. The same can be said

for the giant African crested millipedes that were common on the market in the 1970's but today seem to be represented only by memories. These big gray millipedes with gigantic knobs and crests over the body may have been spirostreptids.

Asia has many large, very colorful millipedes belonging to several families that are virtually unknown in the terrarium. Some are bright red and black and active during the day. South America also has its share of colorful giants, especially species of the genus *Epinannolene*. If importers would get to work and bring in a few more species, millipedes might actually catch on. Certainly there is no shortage of beautiful, interesting, and virtually unknown species waiting to enter the hobby.

INTRODUCING CENTIPEDES

I have to admit that I am not personally enthralled by centipedes. I find them too nervous to make great pets, very delicate, and sometimes dangerous. However, if you like scorpions and tarantulas you probably have at least a hidden desire to own a giant centipede or two. Millipedes and centipedes together traditionally have been considered a subphylum Myriapoda of the phylum Arthropoda, though they are very different in many aspects. For one thing, millipedes are almost exclusively herbivores and scavengers, while centipedes without exception are carnivores chasing down small invertebrate and even vertebrate prey. All centipedes have "jaws" modified as curved poison fangs that are used to grasp the prey and inject small amounts of venom. (The poison fangs or prehensors actually are not true jaws but are the first pair of legs moved forward and changed into jaw-like structures but still constructed more or less like a leg.) There are a few apparently valid incidents where humans have died from the bites of large tropical centipedes, and certainly even the small backyard varieties can cause a painful bite about like a bee sting.

STRUCTURE

Centipedes, class Chilopoda, are flattened, many-legged terrestrial and tree-dwelling arthropods (animals with jointed legs) with poison fangs under the head. There is only one pair of legs per segment, and the number of body segments behind the head may vary from 19 to well over 100, with from 15 to over 160 pairs of legs. Usually the last pair of legs is elongated, heavy, and angled backward. The secondary sex organs are hidden by a set of plates under a small segment between the bases of the hind legs. Eyes typically are absent or

Underside of the head of a large *Scolopendra*. As you can see, the poison fangs or prehensors are really enlarged, modified legs and not true mouthparts. One could say that technically the "bite" of a centipede is actually a venomous "pinch."

Photo: P. Freed

are represented by a few separate ocelli (simple eyes) on the sides of the head (also called the cephalic plate). The antennae are long, multisegmented, and very active. The segments of the body are covered by plates that have grooves characteristic for different genera and species and also may have extended posterior angles or prolongations. Commonly a plate without posterior angles alternates with one with angles. The legs have various combinations of spines on the segments that are very important in correct identification and difficult to see without magnification.

The four major groups (orders) of centipedes fall into two subclasses that have very different developmental histories. In the subclass Anamorpha (for

Taxonomy of centipedes is complex, calling for the determination of many tiny structures, especially hairs and spines under the legs. Notice the deep groove across the first dorsal shield of this *Scolopendra "gigas."* Such grooves often are important characters.

Photo: R. Hunziker

The last pair of legs of centipedes is enlarged and positioned more or less parallel to the line of the body. In this 7-inch Louisiana *Scolopendra heros*, the hind legs are especially thickened.

Photo: M. Walls

the scutigeromorphs and lithobiomorphs) the young leaves the egg with seven pairs of legs and undergoes at least four molts before reaching the adult number of legs (15 pairs) and segments (19). These are small centipedes seldom over 2 or 3 inches (50 or 75 mm) long and of little interest to hobbyists though they are very common in the Northern Hemisphere. The house centipede, *Scutigera coleoptrata*, is found around the world in damp places (bathrooms especially) in human habitations. It feeds on spiders and flies, has long, thin legs with obvious knees, and can run across ceilings, only to fall into the bathtub while you are taking a bath. The bite is mildly venomous, like a bee sting. Lithobiomorphs comprise many families and genera of small centipedes that are found in moist substrates and under rocks. Their taxonomy is based almost entirely on the distribution of spines and hairs (setae) on the legs, and they are virtually impossible to identify. In the northeastern United States the common *Lithobius forficatus* (about 1.5 inches, 35 mm long) from Europe has become established and is abundant in back yards. Few things feel odder than lifting a rock and having a specimen go running up your arm. Ugh! Maybe that's why I don't like centipedes.

The other two groups of centipedes belong to the subclass Epimorpha. These animals are hatched with the full number of legs and segments and simply grow without adding anything to the structure of the body. They always have at least 21 pairs of legs but often have many more. One of the major groups of the Epimorpha is the geophilomorphs, usually extremely elongated, thread-like centipedes with 31 or more pairs of legs (to at least 161 pairs) and a proportionate number of segments. Some are truly imposing animals because of their length (often over 6 inches, 150 mm) combined with extremely thin bodies. The other group of epimorphs is the scolopendromorphs, the "true" centipedes of interest to hobbyists.

This strikingly colored centipede may be a variety of *Scolopendra morsitans*, a large species with distinctive blue-green bands across each segment. Unfortunately, colors are unstable in many centipedes, and variation is poorly understood.

Photo: P. Freed

SCOLOPENDRO-MORPHS

These typical centipedes have 21 or 23 pairs of legs on 25 or 27 body segments. They vary from less than half an inch (12 mm) to over 12 inches (300 mm) in body length, with many tropical species exceeding 8 inches (200 mm). Even the southern United States has species that commonly reach 4 to 6 inches (100 to 150 mm) in length, though average species are closer to 2 inches (50 mm). Many genera are recognized in two or more families, but we are interested mostly in one genus, *Scolopendra*. This genus has four ocelli on each side of the head in combination with some difficult to see characters of spination of the legs. However, almost any centipede over 6 inches (150 mm) long is likely to be a *Scolopendra*. The largest species supposedly is the 10- to 12-inch (250- to 300-mm) *Scolopendra gigantea* from the American tropics, a species that is almost half an inch (12 mm) thick. The largest native species in the United States is *Scolopendra heros*, which ranges from coast to coast in the South (north to Kentucky) and may exceed 8 inches (200 mm) in length on rare occasions.

Scolopendrids vary considerably in color, but typically they are a waxy golden yellow to greenish yellow with the head and last segments differently colored, often orange or black. Some species are truly stunning, ranging from solid cobalt blue to bright yellow with green bands across each segment (*Scolopendra morsitans*, a very common tropical species often seen in the hobby). The legs may be colored in strong contrast to the body.

CENTIPEDE SEX

Unlike millipedes, centipedes have the sex organs small and hidden in the body most of the time, so it is difficult or almost impossible to sex them externally. Commonly the last leg pair of males (the legs projecting backward) are considerably thicker than those of females, and the poison fangs also may be enlarged. The external sex organs are within a small segment at the very end of the body. Courtship seems to consist of the male approaching the female while tapping his antennae on the ground and on her body to elicit a

response—if she is aggressive, he withdraws (centipedes often eat each other). If the female seems responsive, the male eventually stops tapping (several hours may pass) and spins a silken web from a special gland at the end of the body. With this he lines his tunnel (mating often occurs totally underground and in the dark of night) or at least pads a portion of the ground and then places a whitish spermatophore on the web. He withdraws, and

A female *Scolopendra* protectively coiled around a clutch of newly laid eggs. All the centipedes appear to guard their eggs during development, the female often spending weeks underground without feeding.

Photo: P. Freed

the female moves in and picks up the spermatophore with her genital segment.

The eggs are large white pearls that often number between 10 and 20 in a clutch. All centipedes, as far as known, guard the eggs. The female builds a small nesting chamber in the soil, where she lays the eggs. She coils around them as they are laid, and they are never allowed to touch the ground. She constantly grooms them to remove any trace of dirt or fungus and rubs them with a liquid produced by the genital segment to keep them moist. For one to two months she cares for the eggs without feeding, and she will challenge small predators or even eat her young if disturbed.

The young remain in the nesting chamber for several days to weeks, sometimes feeding on their siblings and molting several times. They soon leave the chamber to hunt for food and are on their own. Sexual maturity is reached in perhaps six months, and with luck they can live five or six years.

GENERAL CARE

Centipedes are animals that feel most at home when touching the substrate, so they can be kept in terraria of appropriate size about half filled with potting soil or orchid bark. If you expect to see them on the surface, they will need cover and should be kept as dark as possible (use a red or blue bulb to observe their activities). The cage must have a tight-fitting lid and can be covered with a plastic sheet to increase humidity in the terrarium. These are animals that can climb nearly smooth surfaces, can run backward, and are flat enough and strong enough to wedge themselves through two surfaces that to the eye are actually touching. They can and will escape from most terraria unless precautions are taken. Give them a shallow dish filled with foam or cotton to which water is added at regular intervals; they will drink from this.

Larger centipedes are less likely to need high humidity than smaller ones, and many of the larger species come from relatively dry habitats, either plains and deserts or the branches of trees. Judge the humidity level by how stressed your specimen appears to be. Bromeliads and other plants provide good refuges, but they are dangerous in that you cannot always easily locate the centipede when you go in to feed or clean the cage.

Centipedes must find their own food to kill and eat it. If you wave a cricket in the face of a centipede it will ignore it or just panic and run off. Centipedes use their antennae to locate moving prey and they then bite it several times with the poison fangs to kill it. The prey is then chewed from the spots of the body weakened by the previous bites. In captivity centipedes feed well on mealworms and on crickets with the hind legs removed. In nature they feed on almost any insects they can catch, plus sometimes earthworms and spiders. Large tropical species have been seen

This 8-inch specimen of *Scolopendra subspinipes*, the Vietnamese black centipede, represents a species often seen in the shops. Such a specimen has a painful bite that may cause numbness for hours. Allergic reactions to the bite are not uncommon, and at least one or two deaths are verified. Large centipedes may not be suitable pets in homes with children and roaming pets.

Photo: P. Freed

catching and killing small lizards, though this must be exceptional.

If you have problems getting your centipede to eat in the terrarium, try reducing the space between it and the prey. Put them in a smaller plastic box in one part of the terrarium, which should allow the centipede to more rapidly discover the food.

SELECTION

Identification of the various species of larger centipedes offered for sale currently is difficult or impossible. Though there are relatively few species in *Scolopendra* itself (the home of all the true giants), there are several other related genera (*Hemiscolopendra*, etc.) with very large species. The family Scolopendridae is distinguished from related groups most easily by looking for a cluster of four ocelli at each front corner of the head; *Scolopendra* differs from *Hemiscolopendra* by having a heavy spine under the outer end of the proximotarsus (second segment following the claw) of the legs. Species characters are based on such details as the grooving of the dorsal plates, distribution of fine hairs on the antennae, and number of spines under the hind legs; coloration is variable in most species. *Scolopendra viridis* (2.5 inches, 60 mm, bright green with yellow legs), *Scolopendra alternans* (8 inches, 200 mm, bright yellow overall), and *Hemiscolopendra punctiventris* (2 inches, 50 mm, distinctly blue-green) are common Florida species often sold by dealers as

The reddish head, bright yellow legs, and black end segments of the body are typical of *Scolopendra heros*, a giant centipede found through much of the southern U.S. The body may be greenish black (as in this Louisiana specimen) to pale straw yellow.

Photo: M. Walls

"giants," though only *S. alternans* truly fits that description. The blackish green, red-headed, yellow-legged *S. heros* often enters the market from the Southwest, while several tropical species (including the giant and dangerous *S. morsitans*, yellow with a broad dark green stripe across each plate posteriorly) are imported from uncertain localities.

It is not always easy to find a good captive centipede. I've seen few large specimens for sale, though dealers often hype perfectly ordinary 2- and 3-inch (50- and 75-mm) *Scolopendra* species as "baby giants" that will grow to 10 inches. By the time a centipede is large enough and active enough to make itself available for capture, it should be almost fully grown. Remember that most reach maturity in just six months and live five or more years. A captive centipede may molt and grow a bit in the terrarium, but don't expect miracles. Go on the basis that what you see is what you get. Always check to make sure that the antennae are complete and functional. These are the centipede's eyes for all practical purposes, and it cannot feed without them. A missing or incomplete leg or two, especially

the elongated hind legs, should be no problem, as centipedes often voluntarily drop a leg when confronted with a predator. However, there should be no breaks in the body wall at the base of a leg or between the segments of the back. If you damage the body of a centipede it probably will die rather than heal. It is very easy to open the body cavity of a centipede when picking it up with forceps or chasing it about under a log. If you must handle your centipede, chase it into a bottle with a small mouth instead of trying to pick it up. Remember that the bite from a large centipede may be much more dangerous or at least more painful than the sting of most common scorpions and certainly than the bite of any common tarantula.

Though they are problematic animals in the terrarium, the unusual body form and sometimes interesting coloration of larger centipedes draw the attention of hobbyists looking for an extraordinary pet. Photo of *Scolopendra polymorpha* (Arizona).

Photo: G. & C. Merker

Page numbers in **bold** represent photographs

Abacion, 36, **37**, 38
African black millipedes, **4**, **28**, 44-48, **45**, **46**
Anal valves, 5
Apheloria, **11**, **41**
Aphistogoniulus, **1**, **26**, **54**, 54-55
Archispirostreptus, **4**, **28**, 44-48, **45**, **46**
Atopetholids, 53, **53**
Brachycybe, **10**, **34**, **35**, 35-36
Centipedes, classification, 57-58
Centipedes, reproduction, **59**, 59-60
Centipedes, structure, 56-57
Centipedes, terrarium care, 60, 62
Chicobolus, **50**, 51
Chilognatha, 10
Collum, 6
Cyphopods, 6, **14**
Euryurids, **3**, **40**, 42-43
Eye patch, 5
Floridobolus, 53-54
Giant African millipedes, **4**, **28**, 44-48, **45**, **46**
Globotherium, **9**, 10, **13**
Gnathochilarium, 6
Gonopods, 7, 14-16
Helminthomorpha, 10-12
Julid millipedes, 38-39
Lithobius, 58
Madagascan giant millipedes, **1**, **26**, **54**, 54-55
Millipedes, chemical secretions, 33
Millipedes, definition, 4-5
Millipedes, development, 20-22, **21**, **22**, **23**

Millipedes, egg-laying, 19-20
Millipedes, feeding, **29**, 30-32, **30**
Millipedes, fossil, 5
Millipedes, legs, 6-7
Millipedes, mating, 13-19
Millipedes, sexing, 16, **16**, **17**, 18, **18**
Millipedes, structure, 5-7
Millipedes, terrarium care, 25-30
Mites, commensal, **31**, 32
Narceus, 20-22, 51, **51**
Orthoporus, **6**, **24**, 47, **48**, 48-51
Oxidus, 20-22, **38**, 39-40
Pachydesmus, **6**, **7**, **14**, **41**
Paranota, 7
Penicillata, 8
Pentazonia, 8-9
Pill millipedes, 8-9
Pillbugs, 5
Platyrachidae, **3**, **40**, 42-43
Polydesmida, 12
Polydesmids, 43
Polyxenus, 8
Pseudopolydesmus, **42**
Repugnatorial pores, **32**, 33
Scolopendra, **56**, **57**, **58**, 58-59, **61**, **62**, 62-63, **63**
Scolopendromorphs, 58
Segments, 5
Sphaerotherium, **8**, 10
Spirobolida, 11-12
Spirostreptida, 12
Telson, 7
Tylobolus, **16-18**, **21**, 51-52, **52**
Western desert millipedes, **6**, **24**, 47, **48**, 48-51
Xystodesmids, 40, 42